To Beverly –
Enjoy Douglas,

Sr Pat

Best Wishes!
Mary Hutzunot

Douglas,
the Boy Who Knew God

Douglas,
the Boy Who Knew God

by

Patricia A. McCarthy and illustrated by Mary Heitzenrater

ISBN # 0-9760210-0-5
Printed in the United States of America

First Printing

This book is lovingly dedicated to
Paul Peter Healy, Joseph Wiener,
Meg Moore, Alex Van Slyck, Alex Krueger,
Elizabeth Bean, Tara Anne Zecchini, Cathal Joseph Hickey, Douglas,
and all special children.

They are God's great blessings to us.

Acknowledgments

"My soul proclaims the greatness of the Lord

and my spirit exults in God my Savior."

(Luke 1:46,47 in The Jerusalem Bible)

My gratitude to Douglas and all the patients and workers at Willowbrook State Hospital in New York City. They taught me compassion, hope, and joy. From them I learned that differently abled is not disabled.

Many artists found the subject too difficult. I congratulate Mary Heitzenrater for seeing with the pure eyes of youth. She understood the gratitude and recognized the mystic in a little boy's soul. Her work bears the beauty of her being. I thank her teacher, Helen Mooz of Mercy High School in Middletown, Connecticut. She always turns loose the artist in the souls of teenagers. I also thank the principal of a school that encourages young women to grow into people of grace and mercy. For twenty-five years, Mercy High School has been under the leadership of a woman of mercy, Sr. Mary McCarthy.

My mother, Mary McCarthy, returned to God while I was working on this book. Gratitude was her song and she sang it beautifully for ninety-three years. I say, "Thank you."

For those who are inspired and touched by this story, it is a chapter in my book, *The Scent of Jasmine, Reflections on Peace in Everyday Life,* published by The Liturgical Press of Collegeville, Minnesota.

Douglas,
the Boy Who Knew God

Once upon a time, a little baby boy was born in a very large hospital in a very large city. His name was Douglas. When the other babies left the hospital to go home, Douglas stayed. Douglas looked like the other babies, but he couldn't move his arms or legs. Douglas couldn't even move his head. He was sick and he had no family. The nurses and doctors loved Douglas. They fed him and rocked him and sang to him.

Sometimes the other boys had their mommies and daddies come to hold them and read to them. Douglas didn't have anyone to visit him. The other families would talk and listen to Douglas. He had learned to talk when he was four years old. Because his muscles were weak, talking was hard. Douglas spoke very, very, slowly; and his words were always kind. Everyone liked Douglas.

When he was two years old, Douglas moved to an even bigger hospital. This one had forty buildings. Douglas lived in Building 21 with other little boys. The nurses and aides in his new home loved Douglas. Every day someone rubbed his legs and arms to help Douglas grow stronger. They also taught Douglas how to hold his head straight. It was hard work and sometimes Douglas could do it. When he was tired, Douglas just leaned his head on his shoulder.

Douglas had his own wheelchair like all the other boys, but Douglas always had to be buckled in so he wouldn't slip, and someone also had to push him.

When Douglas was thirteen years old, a new teacher came to the hospital. Her name was Maria. She was very young and very pretty. All the boys liked her. They could tell Maria thought that each one of them was special.

Maria came on Sundays and taught the boys about
God. They learned about Jesus and his love for them.

At the same time that Maria was teaching in Building 21, many people in the hospital went to Building 3 to pray and worship God. One day the boys asked why they couldn't go. Maria told them she couldn't push all the wheelchairs.

The boys were sad. They wanted to pray with everyone else.

Kedrik, a helper in Building 21, had an idea. He took care of some older men, and they could push the wheelchairs. Maria was excited and couldn't wait until next week.

The next Sunday a parade of wheelchairs snaked around the hospital grounds from Building 21 to Building 3. Everyone was excited and happy. Now the boys had a special ride every week and a chance to pray with others on Sunday mornings.

They went in all kinds of weather. Sometimes they wore shorts and t-shirts.

Other times they had to wear hats and coats, with scarves wrapped around them and gloves on their hands.

Building 3 was a sacred place on Sunday morning. All the people from the hospital came to pray together. When the boys from Building 21 arrived, everyone clapped and cheered. They always made room for them up front. In a great sea of people, the boys in the wheelchairs were the happiest.

After the boys, Maria, Kedrik, and the elderly men had been doing this for many months, a big storm hit the city. It was blowing and raining so hard that the streets and sidewalks were flooded. Water was pouring down everywhere. It was too wet outside for little boys in wheelchairs.

Maria had to tell the boys that they couldn't go out to pray with everyone else. The boys were sad; they wanted to see their friends and pray with them.

Maria tried to help the children understand that they could pray anywhere—not only in Building 3. She told them how they could talk to God anytime they wanted, wherever they were.

Douglas interrupted Maria. He had something important to say. " I already know about prayer."

Maria asked, "Did someone teach you?"

Douglas answered, "No. I just know how to pray."

It took Douglas a long time to say all these words because he could only talk slowly.

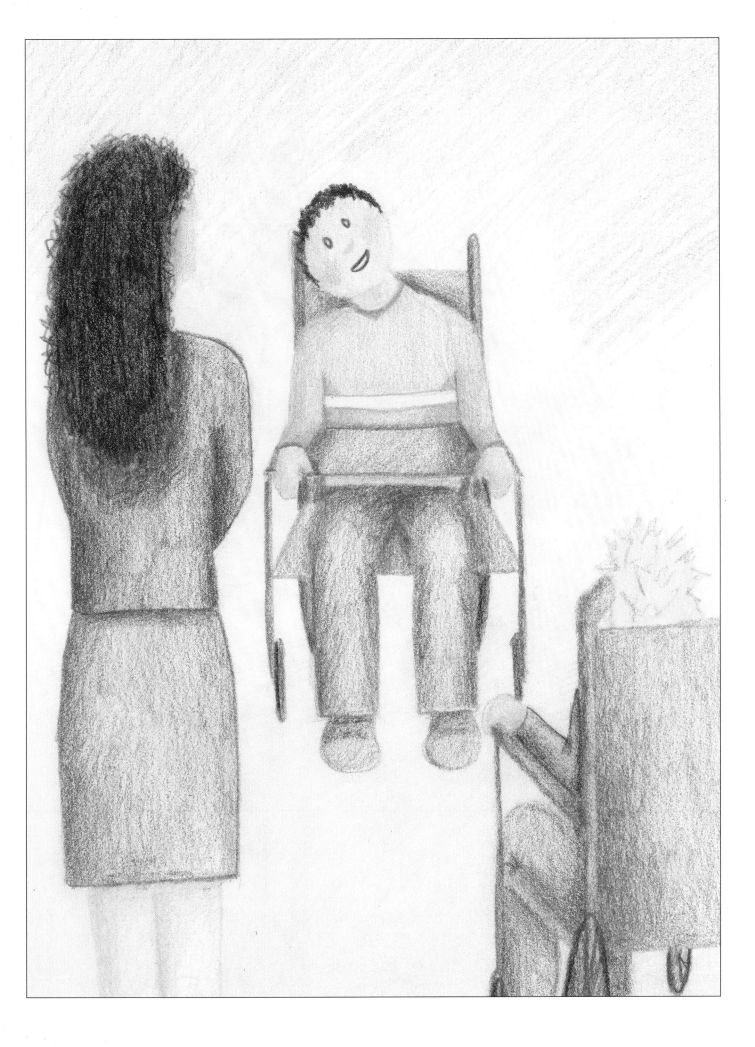

Douglas was so sure of what he was saying and so excited and happy that everyone paid attention to him. Maria
and the other boys listened very carefully as Douglas
struggled to speak.

Douglas told them, "I talk to God every night before I
go to sleep."

Everyone became quiet.

Finally, Maria spoke. "Douglas, what you say to God is special, and you don't have to share it with anyone else. But if you want, you could tell us what you say to God at night. It might help us pray. Do you want to do that for us?"

Douglas said, "Yes."

Then he lifted his head up straight and tall and gave everyone his wide, beautiful smile. In a loud, clear voice, Douglas spoke for the first time without any slowness or hesitation.

He said, "Every night I say 'Thank you'."

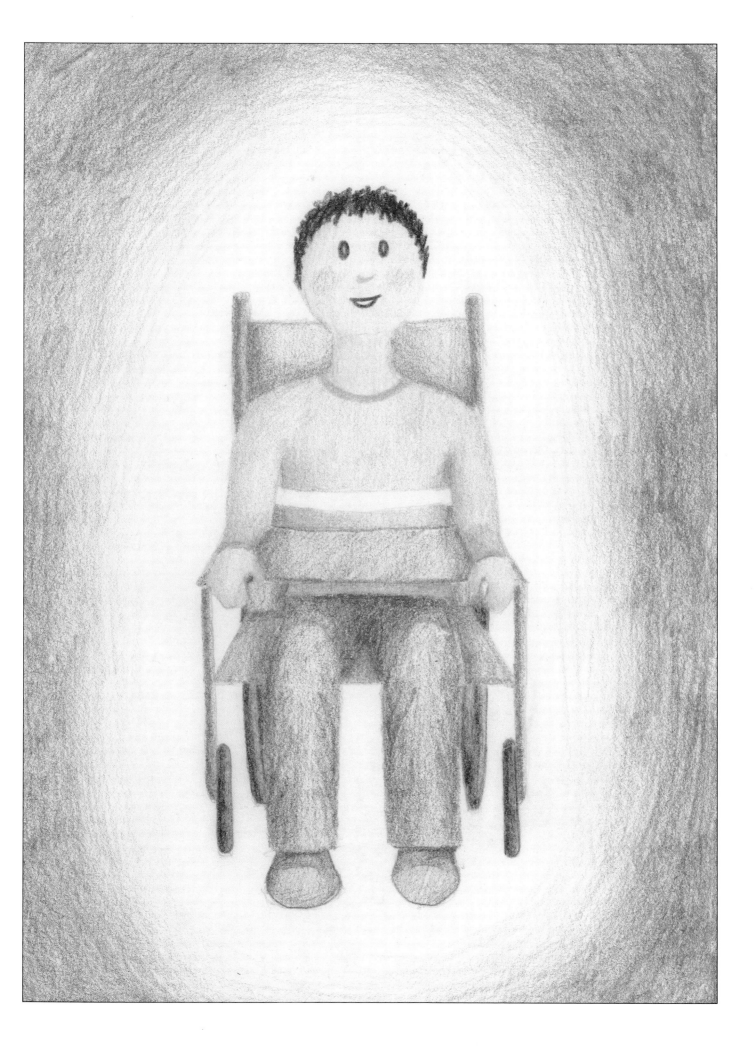